FAIRYTAIL RHODONITE

2

MANGA BY
KYOUTA SHIBANO

BASED ON
A STORY BY
HIRO MASHIMA

C🐦NTENTS

AH HA HA!

I'M FREE...!!

DAMMIT! SEARCH! SEARCH EVERY-WHERE!

THE PRISONER ESCAPED!

NO... WHAT COULD HAVE HAPPENED?!

JUST YOU WAIT, GAJEEL!

Chapter 1: Where is Gajeel?

WHERE IS GAJEEL REDFOX?!

WE'RE BAAACK!

JUVIA!

WELCOME BACK, LEVY-SAN.

ACK!

ONE OF THE MEMBERS OF THE COUNCIL?!!

What's he doing here?

PERHAPS YOU'VE HEARD THE NEWS OF A PRISONER ESCAPING THE OTHER DAY?

JUVIA HAS NO CLUE.

WHAT'S THE DEAL HERE?

ANTED

FLIP

A HEM!

HE SAYS HE'S LOOKING FOR GAJEEL.

HUH?!

GAJEEL HAS BEEN MISSING FOR THE PAST THREE DAYS.

...I SEE.

THEN THIS MIGHT BE... PROBLEMATIC...

AND IT SEEMS HE WASN'T WITH YOU EITHER.

NO.

YOU'RE KIDDING! YOU MEAN YOU WEREN'T WITH HIM?

!!

!

A NEWSPAPER?

I FOUND THIS NEAR GAJEEL'S BED.

WHAT DO YOU MEAN BY THAT?

ISN'T THAT THE SAME POSTER THAT THE COUNCIL MEMBER WAS HOLDING?!

WAIT... DOES THAT MEAN THAT GAJEEL *REALLY WAS*...

WHAT IS THIS ...?!

I AGREE.

THAT WOULD NEVER HAPPEN!

AND THE COUNCIL MEMBER'S ATTITUDE INDICATES THAT GAJEEL IS A SUSPECT,

WHICH MEANS THAT HE MAY BE SOMEHOW CONNECTED TO THIS CRIMINAL...

HOWEVER, HE *IS* MISSING. THAT'S A FACT.

"DETERIORATION OF PUBLIC SAFETY IN BANDIT TOWN OF DENISH..."?

HERE.

THERE WAS A NEWSPAPER ALONG WITH THE WANTED POSTER, AND IF YOU'D LOOK AT THIS ARTICLE...

REALLY?!

...I THINK IT WAS WHERE GAJEEL LIVED.

PRIOR TO HIS ENTRY INTO OUR PREVIOUS GUILD, PHANTOM LORD...

JUVIA HAS HEARD OF DENISH...

GRAY-SAMA IS THE ONLY ONE FOR JUVIA!!

JUVIA JUST HEARS RUMORS NOW AND THEN!

NEVER FEAR THAT JUVIA WAS EVER UNTRUE TO YOU!!

YOU SURE KNOW A LOT ABOUT GAJEEL, JUVIA.

...

WAIT! YOU'RE GOING THERE NOW?!

I SUPPOSE THE BEST WAY THERE IS TO TAKE THE TRAIN.

THE TOWN OF DENISH.

...THAT GAJEEL-KUN'S ABSENCE HAS PUT YOU INTO SUCH A PANIC THAT YOU'D RUSH OFF WITHOUT CONSULTING ANYONE?

I CAN'T WAIT THAT LONG!

YOU SHOULD ASK THE MASTER'S OPINION FIRST!

THE COUNCIL'S MAKING ITS MOVE, YOU KNOW!

LEVY-SAN, COULD IT BE...

...

NO...

HEY!!

I'LL BE IN THE TOWN OF DENISH IF YOU NEED ME!!

ANY-WAY!

TMP TMP TMP TMP

LOVE!!

NO! IT'S NOTHING LIKE THAT!!

SWOON

SHOCK

CRACK

IF IT WAS YOU...

...NONE OF 'EM WOULD BE LEFT ALIVE...

WHAT?

YOU LET 'EM GET AWAY? WHAT A WASTE.

WEST 1-3

...MASH.

HMPH

I NEVER THOUGHT FOR A SECOND THAT *YOU'D* COME TO ME!!

AH HA HA!

PAT

WELL, SINCE WE'RE HERE...

...WHY DON'T WE GO CRAZY FOR A BIT, JUST THE TWO OF US?

GEE HEE!

THE BANDIT TOWN OF DENISH

Chapter 2: My Town

CHATTER ザワ CHATTER CHATTER ザワ

TUNK

AH HA HA HA! THE BOOZE IN THIS BAR IS AS BAD AS IT ALWAYS WAS.

GOT THAT RIGHT!

AND IT STILL HAS THAT WHIFF OF RUSTED IRON IN THE AIR.

NOBODY ELSE SMELLS THAT BUT YOU!

THAT GUY IN THE HOOD... ISN'T THAT MASH?

I HEARD HE GOT SENT TO PRISON EIGHT YEARS AGO...

I GUESS THE NEWS THAT HE BROKE OUT *WAS* TRUE!

SEE THAT GUY NEXT TO MASH?

ALSO ...

DON'T EVEN JOKE ABOUT THAT!! *WE'D* BE THE ONES THE COUNCIL WOULD SEND TO JAIL!

Besides, we wouldn't stand a chance against him!!

HOW ABOUT WE GRAB HIM AND SPLIT THE REWARD?

I THINK IT MAY BE...

BAM

YOU MEAN SANRO PEPPER?!!

IT'S THE DON OF THE PEPPER GANG...

BOOM

COMIN' THROUGH, PUNKS!

GASP

CLACK

CLACK

CLACK

BUT LOOK AT WHAT'S BECOME OF OUR OLD STOMPING GROUNDS...

ENOUGH TO MAKE A MAN CRY.

SO GAJEEL, I GUESS I WAS EXPLORING THE TOWN BEFORE WE MET UP.

WELL, NOT LIKE THERE'S A RULE AGAINST IT OR ANYTHING.

MASH AND GAJEEL...

THE TWO REDFOXES.

THAT'S WHY I THINK THE TWO OF YOU SHOULD JOIN UP WITH MY ORGANIZATION.

THAT'S WHY—

ZSH

WHAT ARE *THEY* DOIN' BACK?

KH!

THE GUY HASN'T CHANGED A BIT!

MRMR

さわ

!!

SO THAT *WAS* GAJEEL!!

NOW, JUST HEAR ME OUT.

HUUH?!

WHO THE HECK ARE YOU?

VSSH

AND JUST WHEN WE WERE THINKIN' THAT, YOU GUYS WALTZED INTO TOWN.

THE RULES OF OUR TOWN ARE ALL OUTTA WHACK. WE WERE THINKIN' OF MAKIN' 'EM RIGHT.

GASP

どよ…

WHADDYA SAY? YOU WANNA TEAM UP AND HELP OUT OUR TOWN?

IF I'M GONNA DO CRIME, I'M GONNA DO *ALL* THE CRIMES!!

BLUNT

WE REDFOXES CAN DO ANYTHING AND EVERYTHING!

WE DO EVERYTHING FROM RUNNIN' CONS TO RUNNIN' TOWNS.

IT'S NO FUN HAVING TO CHOOSE.

I SHOULD HAVE EXPECTED AS MUCH FROM THE REDFOXES.

HEH

MAKES SENSE.

OH?

BUT BEFORE THAT, THERE'S JUST ONE THING.

THAT'S... GAJEEL ...!!

YOU GOTTA BE KIDDING ME!!

HE TOOK OUT THE TOP MOVERS HERE IN AN INSTANT ...?!

STOMP

PEOPLE OF DENISH, DO YOU REMEMBER NOW?!

THE TWO REDFOXES ARE THE KINGS OF THIS TOWN!!

AND NOW WE'RE GOING TO BRING DENISH BACK TO ITS FORMER GLORY!!

WHO RULED DENISH TEN YEARS AGO?

IT WAS US!!

AND THAT'S WHY WE'RE BACK!

GAJEEL !!

MASH !!

YAAAH っ

YEEAAH !!

Y,...

DRINK YOUR FILL, BOYS!!

LET'S ALL RAISE A MUG IN CELEBRATION!

DRINKS ARE ON ME!

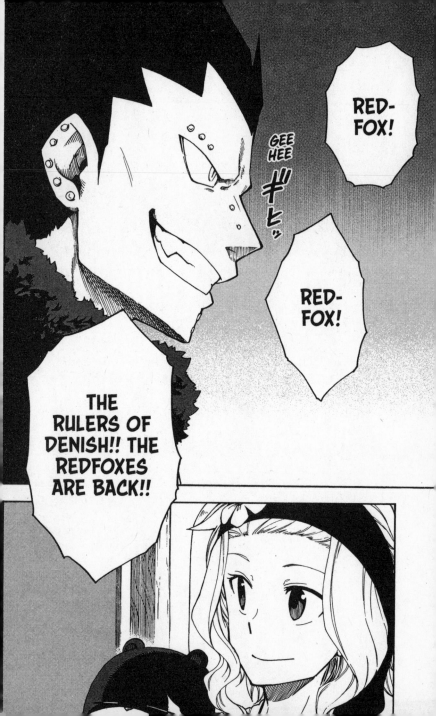

Chapter 3: A Meeting in Denish

RED-FOX?

GAJEEL
...

ピク...

TWITCH

THAT IS AN OBVIOUS LIE!!

NEVER HEARD OF 'IM...

HE'S THE GUY PICTURED ON THIS BEER BARREL RIGHT HERE!

ガジル酒 GAJEEL Beer

HE'S TELLIN' YOU THAT HE'S GOT NO INFO TO SPILL TO YOU FOLKS.

GAJEEL IS IN THIS TOWN, ISN'T HE?!!

LISTEN UP, LITTLE LADY.

!!

SHIK

SURROUNDED

"HAUL HIM BACK IN"...?

"BOSS"?

YOU WANNA HAUL BOSS GAJEEL BACK IN, RIGHT?

I'VE SEEN THAT MARK. YOU'RE FAIRY TAIL WIZARDS, RIGHT?

SO WHERE IS GAJEEL?

GAJEEL IS A MEMBER OF FAIRY TAIL!

WHAT'S THE MATTER WITH OTHER MEMBERS COMING TO SEE HIM?

SO GET LOST!

THE BOSS AIN'T NO MEMBER OF FAIRY TAIL!

HE'S ONE OF US!

HMPH

YEP.

SST

BUT STILL, THAT PRETTY MUCH CONFIRMS THAT GAJEEL IS IN THIS TOWN.

THEY SEE US AS ENEMIES.

WHAT WAS THAT?

AND IF GAJEEL HAS A REASON TO BE HERE...

SHIK

...THEN WE'LL HEAR IT FROM GAJEEL HIMSELF!

THIS IS NO "LOVER'S HOLIDAY" !!

IT'S A JOB!!

LET'S GO, JUVIA.

TO BE OFF ON A LOVER'S HOLIDAY WITH GRAY-SAMA...!

I HOPE THAT JERK GAJEEL HASN'T GOTTEN CAUGHT UP IN THIS MESS.

JUVIA SINCERELY DOUBTS THAT...

BUT I NEVER THOUGHT THE JOB WOULD LEAD US HERE.

SO YOU *DO* GET THE SITUATION!

TO CUT OFF SUPPLIES OF MAGIC NARCOTICS ON THE BLACK MARKET, YES?

!!

UGH! WE ARE *NOT* A COUPLE!

A COUPLE?!

A SWEET COUPLE VISITING OUR TOWN! WHAT A RARE TREAT!

OH, MY!

ARE YOU HERE TO SIGHT-SEE?

THEN WE'D BETTER SHOW YOU SOME OF OUR "HOSPITALITY"! ♪

THAT ISN'T THE FACE OF A MAN SHOWING "HOSPITALITY."

WE'D BETTER SHOW YOU SOME OF OUR "HOSPITALITY"!

OF COURSE!

WE DON'T KNOW WHAT THEY CAN THROW AT US,

SO STAY ON YOUR GUARD!

THAT'S THE GUY WHO ESCAPED FROM THE COUNCIL'S PRISON...

TA-DAAAAAH!

Chapter 4: Illegal Magic Drug

GLEEEM

HE REALLY *DID* MEAN "HOSPITALITY"!!

AND THE GUY JUST KEEPS UP THE PATTER!

CHATTER

OH, AND YOU DO HAVE A PLACE TO SLEEP, DON'T YOU?

NOT SURE IF IT'S TO YOUR LIKING...

NOW GIVE IT A TRY!

JUST CALL ME, BOSS.

IF NOT, I CAN ARRANGE IT FOR YOU!

CHATTER

CHATTER

GOT YA!

CHATTER

WHAT FOR?!

N-NO, THANK YOU. ONE ROOM, PLEASE.

YOU GUYS'LL WANT SEPARATE ROOMS, RIGHT?

THIS GUY...

IS HE REALLY THE ESCAPED PRISONER THE POSTER TALKED ABOUT?

THEN THERE'S SOME THINGS WE'D LIKE TO ASK.

WELL, A LITTLE, I SUPPOSE.

...YOU SEEM...

...LIKE YOU HAVE A LOT OF *INFLUENCE* IN THIS TOWN.

HAVE YOU EVER HEARD OF RHODONITE?

RHODONITE?

WE'RE HERE ON A JOB TRYING TO FIND IT AND CUT OFF ITS SOURCE.

IT'S ALREADY CAUSED PROBLEMS FOR ITS USERS—IT'S CAUSED SOME TO JUST OUTRIGHT COLLAPSE.

IT'S AN ILLEGAL NARCOTIC THAT'S BEEN MAKING THE ROUNDS IN THE UNDERWORLD RECENTLY.

MAYBE YOU HAVE SOME IDEAS ABOUT IT?

THAT'S WHAT ITS USERS ARE SAYING...

AND YOU BELIEVE THAT THIS TOWN IS THE SOURCE OF THIS RHODONITE?

OF COURSE I DO.

IT'S ALMOST ANNOYING.

I'M SURPRISED AT HOW FAST INFORMATION GETS AROUND THESE DAYS.

!!

VWISH

!!

DON'T BE STUPID!!

...YOU'LL LET ME OFF THE HOOK, RIGHT? ♡

I'M AFRAID WE *BOTH* WERE A LITTLE SUSPICIOUS OF EACH OTHER.

I KNEW YOU WERE INVESTIGATING WHEN I TOLD YOU, SO...

SO THAT'S RHODONITE?

FINDING IT WAS EASIER THAN I THOUGHT.

GUESS I HAVE NO CHOICE, THEN.

DIDN'T EXPECT YOU WOULD.

MAYBE SOME PHYSICAL FORCE WILL MAKE YOU RECONSIDER.

SHIIIING

PHYSICAL FORCE, HUH?

OH, MY.

N...

NOW...

...TAKE YOU WITH IT...

...AND HAND YOU OVER TO THE COUNCIL.

...JUST HOLD ON...

SHIK H!!

I THINK WE'LL TAKE THAT RHODONITE, AND WHILE WE'RE AT IT...

...I AM GOING TO BE IN *SO* MUCH TROUBLE WITH GAJEEL!

IF I DON'T GET YOU OUT OF THIS TOWN...

OOPS!

GAJEEL-KUN?

HUH?

He's gonna be mad no matter what I do now...

AAAAAAA!!

HEY, WAIT!

WHAT'S THAT SUPPOSED TO MEAN?!

UGH! MIGHT AS WELL TELL YOU EVERYTHING NOW!

FINE!!

WE'RE ON A JOB!!

WE'RE ON OUR HONEY-MOO—

WHAT ARE YOU DOING IN DENISH?

BLUSH

JUVIA! GRAY!

LEVY-SAN! LILY-SAN!

WHERE'S
GAJEEL?

HE REALLY HIT ME! HARD!

WHEN I CAME TO, I WAS IN THIS ROOM!

WE HAVE NO IDEA WHAT IS GOING ON!

HONESTLY!!

He gave my head a lump!

HUH?

HE HIT ME!

THESE WERE GAJEEL'S ORDERS.

!

WAIT! HEAR ME OUT! JUST HEAR ME OUT!!

CHANK

WHAT ?!

YOU'RE THE GUY ON THE WANTED POSTER!!

WE REALLY NEED YOUR HELP...

FAIRY TAIL!

OUR HELP...?

WHAT'S HE DOING HERE...?!

IT'S ... IT'S GAJEEL?!

GAH!

SO IT WAS YOU PUNKS!

YOU'VE BEEN TRYING TO BRING THAT JUNK CALLED RHODONITE INTO TOWN ON ME!!

I NEVER THOUGHT I'D MEET SOMEBODY AS FAMOUS AS YOU.

YOU USED TO BE THE HERO OF DENISH.

GOTTA BE MY LUCKY DAY!

GAJEEL...

...RED-FOX...

THAT MUCH MAGIC POWER ...!!

THIS MAGIC POWER OF OURS SURE IS SOMETHIN', AIN'T IT?!

TCH!

GH

GH

GH

WITH RHODONITE, EVEN A BUNCH OF THUGS LIKE US...

...CAN WIELD MAGIC THAT MATCHES UP WITH THE TYPE OF WIZARDS YOU GUYS CALL S-CLASS!!

SURE, IT'S ONLY FOR A SHORT TIME...

CLANG

CLANG

CLANG

CLANG

CLANG

...DO YOU REALLY THINK YOU CAN TAKE ON THIS MANY OF US?

NOW, GAJEEL-SAN...

...AND IF WE KEEP USING IT, WE BREAK DOWN, BUT...

CLANG

CLANG

CLANG

CLANG

CLANG

CLANG

THOOM

NOW ANSWER ME THIS!

AND IT'S GONNA STAY LIKE THAT.

EEP!

SHIING

THERE GOES YOUR RHODONITE DEAL. UP IN SMOKE.

!!

STAGGER

WHERE ARE THESE DRUGS REALLY...

IT MAKES YOU FEEL NO PAIN?

SO LOGICALLY, IF A PERSON CAN'T FEEL PAIN ANYMORE...

THAT'S THE REAL VALUE IN RHODONITE.

IT ISN'T JUST ABOUT BOOSTING A GUY'S MAGIC POWER.

IT'S AS IF...

...THEY EACH BECOME AN EVIL WARRIOR ROAMING THE DARK PATHS OF NIGHT—A ROAD KNIGHT.

YOUR ARM COULD BE TORN OFF OR YOUR LEG RIPPED TO SHREDS...

...AND IT STILL WOULDN'T MATTER, I GUESS.

IT IS A DRUG THAT ALLOWS PEOPLE TO KEEP ON FIGHTING AS ZOMBIES DO...

...IS TRYING TO TAKE THAT ON ALL BY HIMSELF?

GAJEEL...

HUH?

HE WAS ALWAYS LIKE THAT.

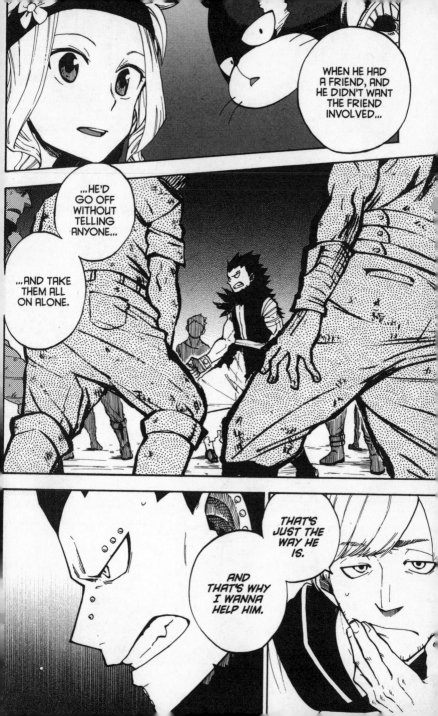

GEE HEE!

DON'T TELL ME YOU...

YOU'RE PRETTY BEAT UP...

ALL BY YOUR-SELF?

SO I GOT RID OF 'EM.

I DON'T LIKE SEEING 'TUDE LIKE THAT WALKIN' AROUND TOWN!

IT JUST GETS ON MY NERVES.

IT DOESN'T MATTER WHO IT WAS—IF GAJEEL DIDN'T LIKE IT...

...HE'D GO OFF ON HIS OWN AND SEND THEM FLYING. THAT'S THE KIND OF KID HE WAS.

I THINK IT'S BEEN MORE THAN 15 YEARS... SINCE GAJEEL CAME TO THIS TOWN.

You're pretty amazing

GEE HEE HEE HEE HEE

SURE.

WE HAD TO DO A LOT OF BAD AND STUPID THINGS TO SURVIVE.

AND YOU TEAMED UP WITH HIM THAT LONG AGO?

WE WENT AFTER SOME RICH FOLK AND ENDED UP CATCHIN' A FEW LUMPS OUR-SELVES.

WE EVEN LEARNED MUSIC FROM TRAVELLING MINSTRELS.

AH HA HA!

Hey, you're really good!

HE WAS ALWAYS SAVING MY BUTT.

WE TRIED TO MAKE A LIVING AS STREET PERFORM-ERS...

...BUT THE PEOPLE OF THE TOWN WOULD ALWAYS SCREAM AT US TO SHUT UP, AND IT'D TURN INTO A BIG ROW!

WE WERE ALWAYS TOGETHER.

IF GAJEEL AND I TEAMED UP...

...THERE WAS NOTHING WE COULDN'T DO.

WE WERE THE BEST TAG-TEAM EVER!

GAJEEL-KUN NEVER SPEAKS ABOUT HIS PAST.

THAT STORY WAS FASCINATING.

...

Well...

AND THEN I WENT AND GOT MYSELF CAUGHT.

Guess I slipped up.

Ah ye...

THE ORIGIN OF THAT TERRIBLE ATTITUDE HE HAD AT PHANTOM LORD.

?

BUT WE FOUND OUT ONE THING.

OH, WELL, IT'S JUST...

WHAT'S WRONG, LEVY?

I GUESS...

I REALIZED I NEVER KNEW ANYTHING ABOUT GAJEEL...

BA-THOOM

GRUNCH

!!

CLANG

CLANG

IT MAY BE GUYS HIGH ON RHODONITE!

IF THERE'S TOO MANY, IT'LL EVEN PUT GAJEEL AT A DISADVANTAGE!

WHAT WAS THAT SOUND...?

IT'S COMING FROM THE HARBOR!!

RIGHT!!

SHK

HE NEEDS YOUR HELP, FAIRY TAIL!!

BOOOM

HUH
?

And what're the Ice Punk and Juvia doing here?!

WHAT'RE YOU JERKS DOING HERE?!

WHEEZE

HUFF

WHEEZE

HUFF

HUNH
?!

...

COME ON! YOU'RE KIDDING!

YOU DEFEATED ALL THESE GUYS...

...ALL ON YOUR OWN?!

GAJEEL...

AT THE COST OF A BODY COVERED IN WOUNDS.

GEH HEH HEH

THAT'S WHY I GOT IT AND YOU DON'T!!

HYAH!

POFF

Chapter 7: Will You Just Shut Up

WHA
—?!

GA-
JEEL?

WHAT DO
YOU MEAN
BY THIS,
GAJEEL...

THESE
GUYS
SPILLED
THEIR
GUTS!

THEY
SAID THAT
THE GUY AT THE
HEART OF THE
RHODONITE
TRADE WAS
YOU...

...MASH!

HEH

I MAY HAVE FALLEN, BUT NOT THAT FAR!

OF COURSE I DIDN'T, YOU DUMMY!

MY, YOU SURE ARE PERSISTENT.

YOU'RE NOT PULLIN' ANYTHING HERE?

SST

WELL, I HAD IT, BUT I'M NO DEALER.

THEN WHY DID YOU HAVE SOME ON HAND?

...THAT THE LIFE WE LIVED TOGETHER WASN'T A LIE!

...MASH.

IT'S TOO BAD...

EVERY SINGLE TIME THAT YOU LIE...

...YOU TOUCH YOUR FACE WITH YOUR LEFT HAND.

AH HA HA HA HA HA HA HA!!

AH HA HA!

!

...HEH.

YOU HAD THAT HABIT EVEN BACK THEN.

I HAD NO IDEA...

A HABIT...? MAKES SENSE...

YOU WERE SO STRONG, THAT STANDING BEHIND YOU, I NEVER THOUGHT YOU...

...SAW ANYTHING THAT I DID.

BUT YOU SURPRISE ME, GAJEEL!

...MEANT THAT WE CRUSHED ANYBODY WE COULDN'T STAND.

THAT WAS ALL THERE WAS TO IT.

MASH!

THE WAY WE USED TO LIVE...

...THAT'S YOU'D GO FOR SOME WORTHLESS DRUG!

I NEVER THOUGHT YOU WERE SO WEAK...

WILL YOU JUST SHUT UP?!!

...THEN IT'S MY JOB TO KNOCK SOME SENSE INTO YOU!

IF YOU'RE DOING SOMETHING YOU SHOULDN'T...

A LECTURE FROM YOU?!

YOU CAME ALL THE WAY HERE JUST TO DO THAT?!

YOU'RE GOOD IN A FIGHT, SO YOU ALWAYS ...

...ACT LIKE YOU'RE SO MUCH BETTER THAN ME!

THAT'S WHAT'S SO ANNOYING ABOUT YOU!

EVEN BACK THEN! YOU'VE ALWAYS BEEN LIKE THAT!

DAMMIT!

ゲーシ
SCRATCH

はぁっ
SIGH

ゲーシ
SCRATCH

NO ONE ASKED FOR YOUR HELP, BUT HERE YOU COME, TRYIN' TO SAVE ME!

DAMMIT!

...THAT YOU WERE ACTUALLY PAYING ATTENTION TO ME.

I WISH I KNEW A WHOLE LOT SOONER...

!

MASH ...

YOU OWE US FOR THIS, GAJEEL.

YOU JERKS ARE...

...WE WON'T ALLOW ANYONE ELSE TO GET INVOLVED!

CHANK+!!

YOU'RE ALWAYS ONE STEP AHEAD OF ME!

YOU'RE *ALWAYS* THE ONE THAT CHANGES!

BEFORE I DO!

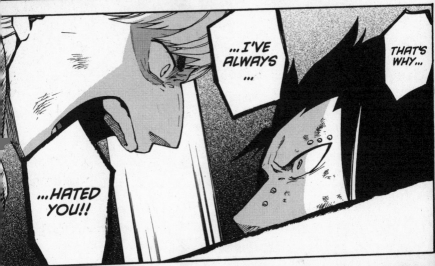

...I'VE ALWAYS...

THAT'S WHY...

...HATED YOU!!

GACLANNG

GA-JEEL!

ONCE I KILL YOU...

...I'LL...

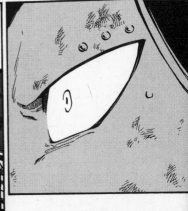

...HAVE A VIEW OF THE WORLD WHERE YOU'RE NOT IN IT!!

WHAM WHAM WHAM WHAM WHAM

...I GET IT NOW.

MASH...

....!!

GAJEEL!!

I ALWAYS THOUGHT WE WERE FRIENDS, BUT...

...I GUESS I WAS THE ONLY ONE THINKING THAT! DAMMIT!

STAGGER

Chapter 9:
Man Behind
the Curtain

HEH

YOU'RE GONNA...

...TURN ME OVER TO THE COUNCIL?

KOFF

KOFF

DAMMIT...

OR MAYBE *YOU'RE* GONNA KILL ME?

...WELL, THAT'S YOUR OWN BUSINESS.

IF YOU DECIDE TO GO OFF AND DIE IN A GUTTER AFTER THIS...

DON'T TALK STUPID!

I JUST COULDN'T STAND YOUR ATTITUDE, SO I HIT YOU. THAT'S ALL.

YOU WANNA DIE, THEN KILL YOURSELF OFF!

GAJEEL...

TCH!

KOFF

...

...

WAIT! YOU GOT NOTHING TO SAY TO ME?!!

IT'S ALL OVER HERE.

WE'RE GOIN' HOME, LILY.

STOMP スタ

STOMP スタ

STOMP スタ

THE REST IS YOUR JOB. DO WHAT YOU WANT.

ANY- WAY ...

THIS IS WHERE MY PART IN THIS ENDS.

HE IS TOO EMBAR- RASSED.

SHUT UP, JUVIA!!

DON'T YOU THINK IT'S FISHY?

HOLD IT.

WHAT'S FISHY?

!!

IT HASN'T BEEN ALL THAT MANY DAYS SINCE HE BROKE OUT OF PRISON.

...BUT THE AMOUNT THAT'S OUT THERE AND THE NUMBER OF PEOPLE HURT BY IT ARE TOO MANY JUST FOR HIM.

HE SAID HE WAS MOVING THE RHODONITE, AND I ACCEPT THAT...

THAT GUY, MASH.

I WENT OUTTA MY WAY TO GET YOU OUT OF PRISON...

...AND FRONT YOU THE VERY BEST RHODONITE I CAN MAKE...

I THINK I SHOULD EXPECT A BETTER OUTCOME THAN THIS, RIGHT?

...!

I EXPECT AT LEAST...

...AN "APOLOGY," OF COURSE.

!!

THAT'S RIGHT. YOU NEVER NOTICED, DID YOU?

IN OTHER WORDS, THE ONE WHO WAS PULLIN' THE STRINGS ALL THIS TIME...

...WAS YOU?

YOU SHOULDN'T BE RELAXING, YOU KNOW!

NOW JUST A MINUTE!

THAT FIGURES.

SO I'VE BEEN THINKING THAT WE CAN RESOLVE EVERYTHING BY BREAKING SOME OF YOUR BONES.

...AND BEHIND THE RHODONITE TRADE.

YOU'RE THE GUY WHO BROKE OUT OF THE COUNCIL'S PRISON...

...AND YOU WERE BEHIND GAJEEL'S DISAPPEARANCE...

SHFF

BUT IT'S A REAL SHAME, Y'KNOW?

KA-SHK

YOU FAIRY TAIL FOLKS ARE JUST BRIMMIN' WITH CONFIDENCE, AREN'T YOU?

THAT YOU'RE IN MY TERRITORY RIGHT NOW.

FWOOSH

Chapter 10: Friends

THESE GUYS ...!!

IT HAS AN INGREDIENT THAT DULLS A WIZARD'S SENSES.

ドォ
GUH!
GRUNCH

HEH HEH HEH.

THIS GREEN FOG IS MADE OF A SPECIAL TOXIC MIST.

...I THINK I'LL GIVE MASH A LITTLE BIT OF THIS TO CHEW ON.

BUT BEFORE I DO...

ス SST

Brain was

AND I'LL BE LONG GONE WELL BEFORE THE FOG CLEARS UP.

YOU THINK I'M STUPID ENOUGH TO TAKE FAIRY TAIL HEAD-ON? DON'T MAKE ME LAUGH!

IT'S A BRAIN-WASH DRUG.

WHA—?!

I'M GOING TO CHANGE SOME OF YOUR MEMORIES.

HEY, SOMEBODY'S GOTTA TAKE THE FALL. LOOKS LIKE THAT WILL ALL BE ON YOU!

WELL, I SUPPOSE THIS IS WORTH MUCH MORE THAN THAT "APOLOGY" I WAS EXPECTIN' FROM YOU.

DON'T TELL ME THIS WAS YOUR PLAN RIGHT FROM THE START, WAS IT?!

KOFF

BUT LET'S FACE THE FACTS—WEAK GUYS LIKE YOU ARE ALWAYS GONNA END UP ON THE BAD END OF A BARGAIN. IT'S YOUR DESTINY.

MASH...

...YOU DID ALL OF THAT YOURSELF.

...AND MAKING DENISH A STRONGHOLD FOR RHODONITE...

YOUR BREAK-OUT...

...GETTING INTO THE DRUG TRADE...

THK THK THK

WHAM

BOOM

SHIK

AND ONCE THE JOB'S DONE, THE GUILD JERKS GET PAID AND THEY CAN'T COMPLAIN.

ALL YOU HAVE TO DO IS LET THOSE ROCK-HEADS IN THE COUNCIL CAPTURE YOU.

AND ONCE YOU'RE CONVICTED, THE JOB'S DONE.

ANY-WAY...

I DOUBT ANYBODY WILL COMPLAIN WHEN YOU TAKE THE FALL.

I MEAN EVEN YOUR OLDEST FRIENDS HAVE ABANDONED YOU, RIGHT?

HA HA HA HA!!

Chapter 11: Rhodonite

YOU REALLY ARE STRONG, GAJEEL.

...BE ABLE TO KEEP UP WITH YOU.

I DOUBT I'LL EVER...

RHODO-NITE...

THE STUFF THAT MAKES PEOPLE INTO DARK ROAD KNIGHTS...

GAJEEL'S BELOVED HOMETOWN IS BACK TO NORMAL, AND WE'VE DONE MORE THAN ANYONE BARGAINED FOR.

WE'VE GATHERED UP ALL THE RHODONITE CIRCULATING THROUGH THE TOWN...

...SO THE CASE IS CLOSED.

AND THAT GUY MASH...

...I GUESS HE GOT INVOLVED WITH RHODONITE BECAUSE HE WAS ALWAYS LOOKING UP TO GAJEEL.

GAJEEL CAME TO A DARK TOWN FULL OF OUTLAWS AND BANDITS, AND HE CLEANED IT UP.

THERE IS A STONE WITH THE SAME NAME, RHODONITE.

DID YOU HEAR, LEVY...

GAJEEL IS ONE MAN, BUT HE HAS MANY ASPECTS.

WHEN GIVEN AS A GIFT, IT HAS THE MEANING OF SOMEONE WHO HOLDS HIS FRIENDS AND FAMILY VERY CLOSE.

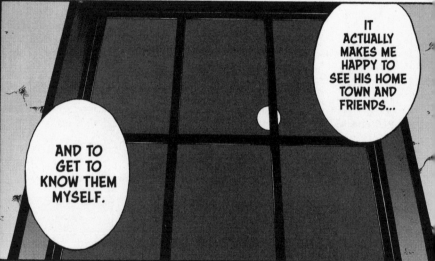

IT ACTUALLY MAKES ME HAPPY TO SEE HIS HOME TOWN AND FRIENDS...

AND TO GET TO KNOW THEM MYSELF.

AAA!

ド THOOM

...

YEAH.

Urgh...

I DID A BAD THING...

I CAN'T TAKE ANOTHER DRINK...

DRUNK BEFORE YOU KNOW IT.

HEY, YOU! WHAT'S THAT GETUP FOR?

HUNH?

THE YEAR IS X791. IT HAS BEEN ABOUT A HALF YEAR SINCE FAIRY TAIL DISBANDED.

ON THE BAMBINA HIGHWAY JUST OUTSIDE THE BAMBOO FOREST...

Chapter 12: First Bout

WE DON'T WANT TO GET CAUGHT UP IN THIS!!

GO FASTER! FASTER!

WHAT? WHAT?

WHAT IS THIS?!

YEAH!

IT'S IN THE VICINITY OF THE BAMBOO FOREST. A FEW LOCALS SAY THEY SAW HIM...

SOMEONE HAS SIGHTED COBRA, YOU SAY?

FIFTH RANKED MEMBER OF THE TEN WIZARD SAINTS

JURA NEEKIS

HE HAD ESCAPED PRISON AFTER THE PREVIOUS COUNCIL WAS ATTACKED.

ONE OF MANY ESCAPED PRISONERS FROM THAT TIME, IT SEEMS.

HMM...

IF HE IS MOVING ALONE AND UNAIDED, THIS MAY BE OUR CHANCE.

GLANCE

AND I HAVE WORK OF MY OWN TO DO...

I'M AFRAID THE ONLY PERSON WITH THE TIME TO HANDLE THIS IS...

HMMM...

OUR INVESTIGA-TIVE FORCE IS VASTLY UNDER-MANNED.

STILL...AS MUCH AS I WOULD BE ENCOUR-AGED BY HIS RECAPTURE...

...THE RESOURCES OF OUR NEW COUNCIL ARE FAR FROM SUFFICIENT.

YOU'RE OKAY ...?

KIDS...IN SHACKLES?

DON'T TELL ME YOU WERE RESCUING THOSE KIDS...

WHY WOULD COBRA DO THAT...?

Chapter 13: Slave Trade

AND THAT'S WHY THIS HAPPENED?

THOSE MEN JUST SUDDENLY ARRIVED...

...AND FORCED US INTO THEIR CARRIAGE.

THESE PAST SEVERAL MONTHS WHILE THE COUNCIL WAS BUSY REFORMING...

YEAH. THE SLAVE TRADE.

YOU HAVEN'T HEARD ABOUT IT?

CHURCH AFTER CHURCH HAVE BEEN ATTACKED.

IT'S ESCAPED CONVICTS LIKE YOU THAT'VE BEEN KEEPING US SO BUSY!

SO DON'T GET SO UPPITY!

WHAT KINDA WORK HAVE YOU JERKS BEEN DOING ALL THIS TIME?!

HUH?

RUMBLE RUMBLE RUMBLE RUMBLE RUMBLE RUMBLE RUMBLE

SNIFF

N...NO...

HUH?

YOU DON'T UNDERSTAND... WE'RE NOT THE ONLY ONES...

QUI...
QUIT YER CRYIN'!!

GUSSH

WAAH...

SO THEY WENT AND GOT ANTHER GROUP OF KIDS BEFORE THEY GOT THESE?

THERE WAS ANOTHER CARRIAGE THAT WENT OFF BEFORE OURS DID.

IT HAD MY BIG BROTHER, MY BIG SISTER, EVERYBODY...

HOW'RE WE SUPPOSED TO SURVIVE...?!

WHAT'LL WE DO?! IF THERE'S NO PLACE FOR US ANYMORE...

IF EVERYBODY'S FAMILIES GET BROKEN APART...

STOP YOUR BLUB- BERIN'!

IF YOU WANNA SURVIVE, YOU JUST START MOVIN' FORWARD!

NO USE IN THAT. ESPECIALLY IF YOUR FAMILY AIN'T AROUND.

WHICH BRINGS ME TO THE POINT...

THIS GUY IS...

DON'T GIVE ME THAT!

YOU'RE PUTTING KIDS IN JAIL?! ARE YOU INSANE?!

WE'RE BEING CAPTURED AGAIN?!

IT HAS A BATHROOM AND THERE ARE TOYS THERE TOO.

WHOA わあっ

LOOK! THEY'RE GETTING LOTS OF SUN, AND THERE'S PLENTY OF FRESH AIR!

WHAT'S WITH ALL THE UNNECESSARY AMENITIES?!

SO THEY CAN JUST RELAX AND WAIT FOR US!

THERE AIN'T NO SAFER, STRONGER CAGE AROUND FOR 'EM!

I'M GONNA GO BUST THE HEADS OF THE JERKS WHO ATTACKED YOUR FAMILIES!

THEN WE'RE ALL GOING BACK TO YOUR CHURCH TOGETHER!

I GUAR-ANTEE IT!

YOU PUNKS ...!!

3D... STAGGER

GH...

THOSE BRATS ARE *MY* PRECIOUS PROPERTY!!

AND I DIDN'T GIVE YOU PERMISSION TO DO ANYTHING WITH THEM!!

KACHAK

Chapter 14: The Infallible Plan

YOU'RE SAYING SOMEBODY CUT OFF THE SLAVE TRANSPORTATION ROUTE?

YES SIR!

THE CARRIAGE WAS LEFT A BROKEN WRECK...

NOW THEY'RE SEARCHING FOR OUR BASE.

WHAT?!

GAJEEL OF THE COUNCIL AND COBRA OF THE ORACIÓN SEIS DID IT.

I SAW IT ALL.

BUT WHY WOULD ONE OF THE SEIS...?

HE HASN'T TEAMED UP WITH GAJEEL, HAS HE? NAW...

IT LOOKS LIKE THE COUNCIL HAS FINALLY SNIFFED US OUT.

I'D SAY IF WE TRIED TO FIGHT 'EM HEAD-ON, WE HAVE A SLIM CHANCE OF WINNING...

...BUT...

...

YOU THINK IT'S OKAY?

SO IF THEY'RE HEADING HERE...

...THERE ARE PLENTY OF WAYS THAT WE CAN SHOW THEM A GOOD WELCOME.

THIS IS MY TER-RITORY!

YOU'RE GONNA TAKE 'EM HEAD-ON?

AIN'T NO REASON TO STRATEGIZE.

DO YOU DOUBT MY EARS?

BUT LOOK. WE'RE HERE AND THEY AIN'T.

IS THIS REALLY SUPPOSED TO BE THEIR BASE?

NO DOUBT ABOUT THAT.

THERE ARE FOUR OF THEM AND SIX HOSTAGES RIGHT HERE.

COMING AT US FROM A BLIND SPOT...

...DON'T MEAN I CAN'T HEAR YOU!

GAH?!

THUD

THEY'RE TOTALLY UNSCATHED ?!

THIS IS BAD!!

WE'RE GONNA TAKE BACK THOSE HOSTAGES NOW!!

NUMBER 62, 63, AND...

...64!!

I ORDER YOU TO PROTECT ME!!

?!!

YOU CAN'T ATTACK WHEN IT'S LIKE THIS!

THAT MAKES SENSE.

HA!

HA HA HA HA HA!!

ZSH

IT TURNS OUT THE SUBORDINATION MAGIC I CAST ON *MY PROPERTY* WAS THE RIGHT THING TO DO!

YOU PIECE OF CRAP...!!

KEEP THE BOTH OF THEM BUSY!!

Chapter 15: Effective Use

WHOOSH

YOU DON'T MIND GETTING THE BRATS CAUGHT UP IN IT?

I DON'T LIKE THE WAY YOU USE MAGIC, YOU JERK!

HOW *ADMIRABLE* OF YOU!

OH? YOU'RE ACTUALLY PROTECTING THE BRATS?!

HEY, IF A BRAT GETS BUSTED UP, THEN ALL I GOTTA DO IS GET ANOTHER BRAT.

I COULDN'T CARE LESS IF THEY DIE!

WHOOSH

BUT USING THEM SHOWED ME YOUR WEAKNESS!!

WHAT WAS THAT...?!

ZWAM BAM BAM

KH!

I DIDN'T EVEN KNOW I COULD USE THEM THIS WAY!!

!

GRAB

THIS IS INCREDIBLE!

THIS SHOULD WORK ON THE COUNCIL AND THE GUILDS!

I CAN EASILY PUT A STOP TO THEM NOW!

SEE, I GOT A LOT OF NEW BRATS TO KIDNAP.

YEAH. THAT'S EXACTLY WHAT YOU'RE GONNA LET ME DO.

SHING

YOU THINK WE'RE GONNA LET YOU GET AWAY?!

HA HA HA HA HA HA HA!!

WHOOSH

SO FEEL FREE TO PLAY WITH THE BRATS UNTIL YOU DROP DEAD!

!!

YOU...

GA-CLANG

GA-CLANG

THEY DON'T EVEN CARE IF THEY'RE HELD BACK?

DAM-MIT!

KRCH

RRG!

RRHG!

RAH!

KRSH

YOU DON'T GET IT, DO YOU?

TRYING TO BE A HERO IS JUST FOR STUPID PEOPLE!

YOU'D BE OUTTA THERE IN NO TIME IF YOU'D JUST KILL THE BRATS.

I'M THE POISON DRAGON OF THE ORACIÓN SEIS, YOU KNOW!

Cobra?

I'M NO COUNCIL MEMBER. AIN'T NO WIZARD FROM SOME OFFICIAL GUILD EITHER.

I DON'T FOLLOW THE SAME RULES THE HEROES DO!

*POISON DRAGON'S ROAR!!!

KRSH

GAH!

GEE HEE

YOU'RE A BAD LOSER!

THE GAME'S ALREADY OVER!

KOFF

ZSH

OKAY, NOW...

!

I DID HOLD BACK...

BUT EITHER WAY, YOU STILL GOT HIT WITH A POISON BREATH ATTACK.

BET YOU'RE WIPED OUT.

FULL POWER

TARGET

SO THAT'S WHAT I FIGURED.

AND IF I WENT FOR A HEAD-ON ATTACK, HE COULDA USED THE KIDS AS HUMAN SHIELDS.

A FULL-OUT BREATH ATTACK WOULD KILL BOTH THE GUY AND THE KIDS.

SO THAT'S WHY YOUR BREATH ATTACK WAS SO WEAK?

HEH!

I COULD HEAR...

...YOUR "VOICES" TOO.

I could hear it.

YOU WERE AS FOOLED AS EVERYBODY ELSE!

TCH!

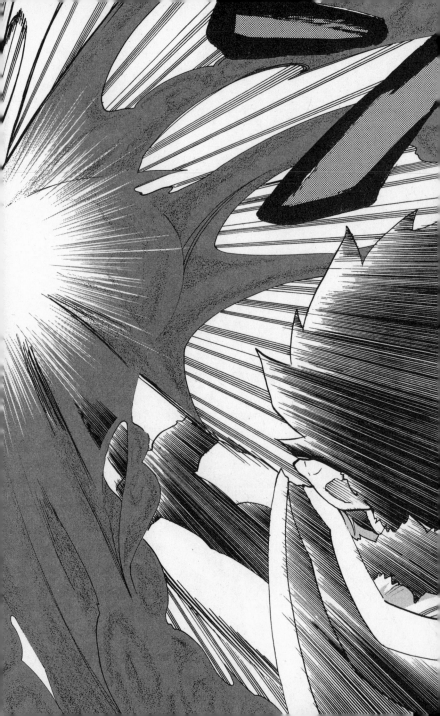

FINISHED WITH WHATEVER BUSINESS YOU HAD?

Final Chapter: The Place to Go Home to

MAC-BETH!

I WOULD ASSUME YOUR ERRAND WAS QUITE VITAL FOR YOU TO HAVE VANISHED ON YOUR OWN.

HEH.

OF COURSE WE DID! WHAT? YOU DIDN'T WANT US TAGGING ALONG?

YOU'VE BEEN MISSING SINCE LAST NIGHT.

AWW, YOU NOTICED?

HONESTLY! THEY'RE ALWAYS GOING OFF DOING STUFF ON THEIR OWN!

DOESN'T IT BOTHER YOU AT ALL, JELLAL?!

NO. YOU SEE, I DON'T INTEND TO BE A CHAIN ON THEM.

...I BELIEVE IT IS TIME FOR US TO TRUST THEM.

BESIDES, SINCE THEY'VE BECOME OUR COMRADES...

THERE IS SOMETHING IN EVERYONE'S HEART OF WHICH THEY ARE UNWILLING TO LET GO.

DON'T LET THOSE NAÏVE THOUGHTS TRIP YOU UP!

I CAN HEAR YOU!

HEH

YOU LET COBRA GO?!

I DID *NOT* LET HIM GO*!!*

THE COUNCIL...

W H A T ?!

HE WAS NEVER THERE FROM THE START.

JUST SHUTTING DOWN THAT SECRET SLAVE ROUTE WAS AN ACHIEVEMENT.

I-I GUESS IT IS, BUT...

YOU KNOW THAT WE'RE SHORT-HANDED!

...TO CHECK THEIR INFO BEFORE GIVIN' A GUY AN ASSIGNMENT.

SO GO TELL THE INTELLI-GENCE GUYS...

I'M GONNA GIVE YOUR COUNCIL THE SLIP!

I AIN'T EVER ENTERING A JAIL CELL AGAIN.

YOU REALLY THINK YOU CAN GET AWAY FROM ME?

SURE.

A PLACE TO GO BACK TO.

I FOUND A PLACE THAT I CAN LIVE FREE.

I GOTTA GO BACK, OR I'LL HAVE EVEN MORE OF 'EM WHINING AT ME!

YOU'RE ALL IDIOTS! YOU, NATSU, AND ALL THE REST!

MAYBE I *SHOULD* ARREST YOU!

THAT'S FAIRY TAIL FOR YOU!

HA!

FAIRY TAIL STILL EXISTS!

IT'S ALMOST TOO BAD IT DOESN'T EXIST ANYMORE.

BUT THAT DOESN'T MATTER TO ME.

THE GUILD HALL MAY BE GONE...

...AND EVERYBODY SCATTERED TO THE WINDS...

SO THAT'S WHY WE HAVE TO DO OUR BEST HERE!

FAIRY TAIL COULD REFORM AT ANY TIME AND PLACE!

COME ON, GAJEEL! SNAP OUT OF IT!

YOUR NEXT JOB!

FLIP

HEH!

IF I GOTTA, THEN I GUESS I GOTTA.

TO BE CONTINUED IN *FAIRY TAIL*

Intermission

YOU'RE DOIN' AN INFILTRATE AND INVESTIGATE GIG?

I AM NOT !!!

I'D SAY HIS INTEREST SHOWS THAT GAJEEL IS WORRIED.

In his own way.

HUH?

AND THEY'RE ACTING A LITTLE SUSPICIOUSLY LATELY.

YEP!

WAIT, I KNOW THIS "AVATAR." IT WORSHIPS ZEREF, RIGHT?

ARE YOU MAKING FUN OF ME?

YOU'RE SO TINY.

WELL, I DOUBT THEY'D FIND YOU OUT.

Grr.

GEE HEE

I AIN'T WORRIED AT ALL!

IF LEVY TRIES, SHE CAN DO ANYTHING BY HERSELF!

WHAT'S WITH YOU?

HUNH?

...

YOU DON'T HAVE TO TELL ME THAT!

DON'T GO SCREWIN' THIS UP.

HM? OH...

NOTH-ING!

AFTERWORD

It's the second volume of Fairy Tail Gaiden!

This time, Gajeel is the main character, and to tell the truth, Gajeel is a Fairy Tail wizard that I particularly like.

And since this story touches on parts of Gajeel's past, it introduces a character by the name of Mash.

Actually, I really worried about whether or not to include Mash.

But even so...and I mentioned this in the last volume's Afterword, but I'm a personal fan of Fairy Tail, and I really like the Fairy Tail worldview. On top of that, I get to work with a wizard I like and get into his past, so I wondered if it's okay to stuff in a character that I created? I mean, really, is that okay...? As manga creator Shibano, this makes me happier than anything, but Fairy Tail-fan Shibano screamed at me for wanting to add an original character, and I couldn't get past that.

And that's why I worry. I mean if it's an enemy character, the hero can hit them, and BOOM, it's over. You don't worry too much about that...

So when I talked to my editor about it he said, "If your enemy character is compelling, doesn't that make the hero (Gajeel) who defeats him even more compelling?"

Hey, that's true!!!!!

If I'm going to draw a really cool Gajeel, I can't have him go up against a half-baked antagonist! And that's how Mash gradually became the character that he is. And I have to say that I'm really liking Mash now.

And although it was a bit of a short story, I had Gajeel do a tag-team with Cobra. Since Gajeel's with the council, and Cobra broke out of the council's jail cell, I thought this might be the perfect chance to team them up. Since neither of them ever actually say what they're really thinking or feeling, I think it gave their dialog a bit of a unique atmosphere.

Anyway, let's meet again in the next volume!

KYOUTA SHIBANO

STAFF: ATSUO UEDA, MINAMI YASAKA, MERIO YUKINA
SPECIAL THANKS: KIMI-C

Translation Notes:

Page 5,
Local Specialty

There's a tradition in Japan that when traveling, every region has a dish or two that is considered their signature dish. Sometimes it's related to the crops grown or animals available in the region and other times related to certain ways of preparing food. The smart traveler researches these before he takes off on his journey, and there are some who simply memorize all the local specialties all over Japan. Some examples include Okonomiyaki (a meat & veggie pancake-like dish) for places like

Hiroshima and Osaka, fried prawns for Nagoya, or Champon (a Chinese noodle dish) for Nagasaki.

Page 23, Don of the Pepper Gang

As the readers probably figured, Sanro Pepper is not named Donald. The Japanese also uses the word "Don," and, of course, it's the same word as we know in the phrase "mafia don." Just for those who don't know, it's originally an Italian word *donno* which

is a word of respect, although it was originally a word for "lord" (it comes from the Latin, *dominus*).

Page 61, Road Knight

IT'S AS IF...

...THEY EACH BECOME AN EVIL WARRIOR ROAMING THE DARK PATHS OF NIGHT–A ROAD KNIGHT.

There are unique aspects of the Japanese language that make the way the Japanese spell Rhodonite exactly the same as the way the Japanese would spell the English words, Road Knight. But in this case, the "road" is referring to a dark, scary road, and the "knight" would be more like a warrior or swordsman. And you wouldn't want to meet a swordsman on a dark road, would you? That's the nuance that is being imparted to the Japanese reader when they read the meaning (in small Japanese letters next to the English words).

MASH

He wasn't a wizard himself, but he was able to use his easy-going conversation style to become a seller of magic items (although it seems an easy-going personality can't successfully sell all items). He also learned swordsmanship for self-defense.

The council became aware of him after he sold defective magic items in a fraud case, and he was jailed. But one thing he kept a secret was that he claimed responsibility for all the actions of his accomplices, allowing them to go free.

He always seemed to rely on Gajeel's overwhelming strength, and because he could never match Gajeel's strength, he started getting jealous. After they talked things over, he returned to jail, and awaited the end of his now-extended sentence.

FAIRY TAIL | **RHODONITE**

MANGA
KYOUTA
SHIBANO

ORIGINAL WORK:
HIRO
MASHIMA

FINALLY, A LOWER-COST OMNIBUS EDITION OF FAIRY TAIL! CONTAINS VOLUMES 1-5. ONLY $39.99!

-NEARLY 1,000 PAGES!
-EXTRA LARGE 7"x10.5" TRIM SIZE!
-HIGH-QUALITY PAPER!

Fairy Tail takes place in a world filled with magic. 17-year-old Lucy is a wizard-in-training who wants to join a magic guild so that she can become a full-fledged wizard. She dreams of joining the most famous guild, known as Fairy Tail. One day she meets Natsu, a boy raised by a dragon which vanished when he was young. Natsu has devoted his life to finding his dragon father. When Natsu helps Lucy out of a tricky situation, she discovers that he is a member of Fairy Tail, and our heroes' adventure together begins.

FAIRY TAIL

MASTER'S EDITION

a Silent Voice

KC

KODANSHA
COMICS

"The word heartwarming was made for manga like this."
–Manga Book-shelf

"A harsh and biting social commentary... delivers in its depth of character and emotional strength." -Comics Bulletin

"A very powerful story about being different and the consequences of childhood bullying... Read it."
–Anime News Network

Shoya is a bully. When Shoko, a girl who can't hear, enters his elementary school class, she becomes their favorite target, and Shoya and his friends goad each other into devising new tortures for her. But the children's cruelty goes too far. Shoko is forced to leave the school, and Shoya ends up shouldering all the blame. Six years later, the two meet again. Can Shoya make up for his past mistakes, or is it too late?

Available now in print and digitally!

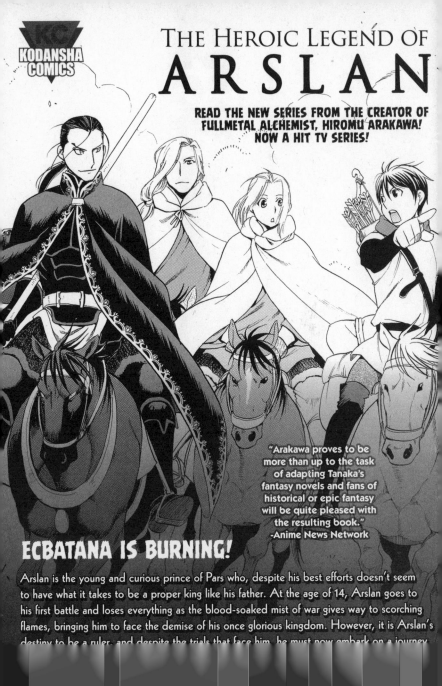

THE HEROIC LEGEND OF
ARSLAN

READ THE NEW SERIES FROM THE CREATOR OF FULLMETAL ALCHEMIST, HIROMU ARAKAWA! NOW A HIT TV SERIES!

"Arakawa proves to be more than up to the task of adapting Tanaka's fantasy novels and fans of historical or epic fantasy will be quite pleased with the resulting book."
-Anime News Network

ECBATANA IS BURNING!

Arslan is the young and curious prince of Pars who, despite his best efforts doesn't seem to have what it takes to be a proper king like his father. At the age of 14, Arslan goes to his first battle and loses everything as the blood-soaked mist of war gives way to scorching flames, bringing him to face the demise of his once glorious kingdom. However, it is Arslan's destiny to be a ruler, and despite the trials that face him, he must now embark on a journey

SANKAREA
undying love

"I ONLY LIKE ZOMBIE GIRLS."

Chihiro has an unusual connection to zombie movies. He doesn't feel bad for the survivors – he wants to comfort the undead girls they slaughter! When his pet passes away, he brews a resurrection potion. He's discovered by local heiress Sanka Rea, and she serves as his first test subject!

KC KODANSHA COMICS

D-EVIL SURVIVOR

デビルサバイバー

AFTER DEMONS BREAK THROUGH INTO THE HUMAN WORLD, TOKYO MUST BE QUARANTINED. WITHOUT POWER AND STUCK IN A SUPERNATURAL WARZONE, 17-YEAR-OLD KAZUYA HAS ONLY ONE HOPE: HE MUST USE THE *"COMP,"* A DEVICE CREATED BY HIS COUSIN NAOYA CAPABLE OF SUMMONING AND SUBDUING DEMONS, TO DEFEAT THE INVADERS AND TAKE BACK THE CITY.

BASED ON THE POPULAR VIDEO GAME FRANCHISE BY ATLUS!

INUYASHIKI

A superhero like none you've ever seen, from the creator of "Gantz"!

Ichiro Inuyashiki is down on his luck. He looks much older than his 58 years, his children despise him, and his wife thinks he's a useless coward. So when he's diagnosed with stomach cancer and given three months to live, it seems the only one who'll miss him is his dog.

Then a blinding light fills the sky, and the old man is killed... only to wake up later in a body he almost recognizes as his own. Can it be that Ichiro Inuyashiki is no longer human?

Comes in extra-large editions with color pages!

Maria
THE VIRGIN WITCH

"Maria's brand of righteous justice, passion and plain talking make for one of the freshest manga series of 2015. I dare any other book to top it."
—UK Anime Network

PURITY AND POWER

As a war to determine the rightful ruler of medieval France ravages the land, the witch Maria decides she will not stand idly by as men kill each other in the name of God and glory. Using her powerful magic, she summons various beasts and demons —even going as far as using a succubus to seduce soldiers into submission under the veil of night— all to stop the needless slaughter. However, after the Archangel Michael puts an end to her meddling, he curses her to lose her powers if she ever gives up her virginity. Will she forgo the forbidden fruit of adulthood in order to bring an end to the merciless machine of war? Available now in print and digitally!

KC
KODANSHA
COMICS

My Little Monster

OPPOSITES ATTRACT...MAYBE?

Haru Yoshida is feared as an unstable and violent "monster."
Mizutani Shizuku is a grade-obsessed student with no friends.
Fate brings these two together to form the most unlikely pair. Haru
firmly believes he's in love with Mizutani and she firmly believes
he's insane.

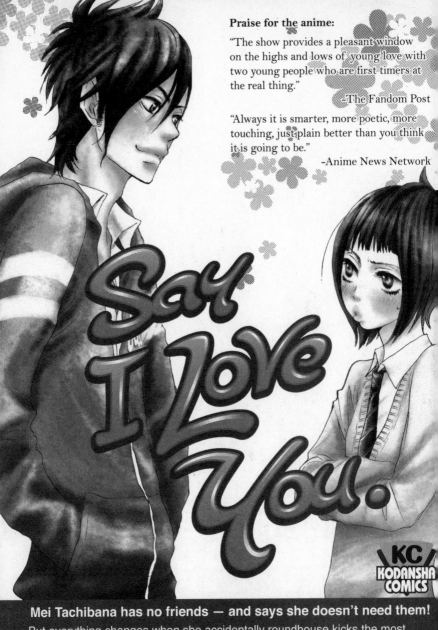

Praise for the anime:

"The show provides a pleasant window on the highs and lows of young love with two young people who are first-timers at the real thing."

—The Fandom Post

"Always it is smarter, more poetic, more touching, just plain better than you think it is going to be."

—Anime News Network

KC
KODANSHA COMICS

Mei Tachibana has no friends — and says she doesn't need them!

But everything changes when she accidentally roundhouse kicks the most popular boy in school! However, Yamato Kurosawa isn't angry in the slightest—in fact, he thinks his ordinary life could use an unusual girl like Mei. But winning Mei's trust will be a tough task. How long will she refuse to say, "I love you"?

NO.6

A PERFECT LIFE
IN A PERFECT CITY

r Shion, an elite student in the technologically sophisticated
ty No. 6, life is carefully choreographed. One fateful day, he
kes a misstep, sheltering a fugitive his age from a typhoon.
lping this boy throws Shion's life down a path to discovering
e appalling secrets behind the "perfection" of No. 6.

KC
KODANSHA
COMICS

SHERLOCK BONES

DEDUCTIVE DOG DETECTIVE

When Takeru adopts a new pet, he's in for a surprise—the dog is none other than the reincarnation of Sherlock Holmes. With no one else able to communicate with Holmes, Takeru is roped into becoming Sherdog's assistant, John Watson. Using his sleuthing skills, Holmes uncovers clues to solve the trickiest crimes. 🐾

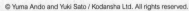

SWAPPED WITH A KISS?!

Class troublemaker Ryu Yamada is already having a bad day when he stumbles down a staircase along with star student Urara Shiraishi. When he wakes up, he realizes they have switched bodies—and that Ryu has the power to trade places with anyone just by kissing them! Ryu and Urara take full advantage of the situation to improve their lives, but with such an oddly amazing power, just how long will they be able to keep their secret under wraps?

Available now in print and digitally!

A Kodansha Comics Trade Paperback Original.

Fairy Tail: Rhodonite copyright © 2016 Hiro Mashima / Kyouta Shibano
English translation copyright © 2018 Hiro Mashima / Kyouta Shibano

All rights reserved.

Published in the United States by Kodansha Comics, an imprint of Kodansha USA Publishing, LLC, New York.

Publication rights for this English edition arranged through Kodansha Ltd., Tokyo.

First published in Japan in 2016 by Kodansha Ltd., Tokyo

ISBN 978-1-63236-634-4

Printed in the United States of America.

www.kodanshacomics.com

9 8 7 6 5 4 3 2 1

Translation: William Flanagan
Lettering: AndWorld Design
Editing: Ajani Oloye
Kodansha Comics edition cover design by Phil Balsman